Vauxhall Cross

First published in Great Britain in 1992 by
Wordsearch Publishing Ltd
26 Cramer Street
London W1M 3HE
Telephone 071 486 7419

ISBN 0 9518284-3-6

Design Patrick Myles
Production Christine King
Additional research Louisa Denman

Printed and bound in Great Britain by
Balding & Mansell plc, Wisbech

Photography : Front cover, 2-3, 6 & 8-9 Jo Reid &
John Peck; 10-11 Tim Motion; 12 Martin
Charles/Alan Williams/Nigel Young; 13 Courtesy
of The Vauxhall Society; 14 Sam Lambert;
18 Graham Challifour; 20-21 Jo Reid & John Peck;
22 Regalian Properties; 26 Jo Reid & John Peck;
30-31 Jo Reid & John Peck; 32-33 Nigel Young;
34 Alan Williams; 35 AA Slide Library/Courtesy of
Regalian; 38 Courtesy of Vauxhall St. Peters
Heritage Centre; 40-41 Jo Reid & John Peck;
42-43 & 46 Dennis Gilbert; 47 Chorley &
Handford/Dennis Gilbert; 51 & 52 Dennis Gilbert;
54 Dennis Gilbert/ Nigel Young; 55 Dennis Gilbert;
58-59 Nigel Young; 61 Dennis Gilbert; 62 Nigel
Young; 63 Dennis Gilbert; 67 Nigel Young;
68-69 Guy Woodland; 71 Jo Reid & John Peck;
72 Niall Macleod; 73 & 74 Dennis Gilbert; 76-77 &
80-81 Jo Reid & John Peck; 82 Niall Macleod;
96 Jo Reid & John Peck; back cover Niall Macleod

Contents

Kenneth Powell

Vauxhall Cross

The story of the design and construction of a
new London landmark

Foreword

It is widely perceived that developers have a responsibility to the community for the buildings which they produce, and even more widely perceived that this responsibility is rarely manifested. Regalian as a company, with its extensive role in Urban Regeneration in the early 1980s, accepted this responsibility before it became fashionable to do so and Vauxhall Cross is a clear manifestation of our commitment to good design and quality construction.

We view the project as more than a mere demonstration of the provision by the private sector of buildings constructed on time, within budget and to the requirements of an exacting client. It is literally a striking demonstration that major capital development projects can be undertaken and implemented provided the developer accepts these responsibilities. The building of distinction which now rises proudly from the south east entrance to Vauxhall Bridge is dedicated to the many people and numerous organisations who, through their endeavours, have made this possible.

David Goldstone

1

Slaying the Green Giant

The river Thames is both a barrier and a chain, linking the collection of settlements that makes up London. Vauxhall Cross lies less than a mile from Westminster Abbey, within sight of the seat of Parliament, and even closer to one of the prime tourist attractions of London, the Tate Gallery. Yet tourists do not generally get to Vauxhall Cross, where a tangle of roads, a six track railway and a collection of mediocre post-war buildings mark what a former environment secretary described as "a major approach to the capital." This is the site of a dramatic new building – one of the great new London monuments of the 1990s – which has finally put Vauxhall Cross on the map of modern London.

The success of this building in putting to use a long-derelict site and creating a public building – which, exceptionally for Britain, is a notable work of architecture – is the result not only of the involvement of an architect, Terry Farrell, with an instinctive feeling for building in cities, but of uncommonly harmonious and efficient working relationships. The developer, Regalian Properties plc, led a team which, unusually, included a buyer and long-term user (Property Holdings/PSA), as well as the usual professional team of engineers, contractors (under the leadership of Laing Management Ltd as management contractors), quantity surveyors and the many other professionals and specialists necessary to put together any large building.

Vauxhall Cross is one of three major "landmark" buildings completed by Farrell in central London. The river links all three: Alban Gate, inland at London Wall, but high

Aerial view of
London showing
the River Thames
which effectively
divides central
London in two,
yet links some of
the city's major
landmarks

12

enough to read on the City skyline; Embankment Place, making a landmark out of what was once a utilitarian railway station at Charing Cross; and Vauxhall Cross, probably the climax of an important phase in Farrell's work. To date, Farrell has been a London architect, though his ambitions now extend beyond London and beyond Britain. His contribution to the new look of London has been both significant and positive – and he is still a young man in the world of architecture. Vauxhall Cross is probably the finest of his large buildings, a clear statement of an approach to architecture that is rooted in a view of the city and of urban life and history.

Vauxhall Cross is tantalisingly close to the modern heart of London, but has traditionally been a place apart. "Cross" not because of any religious associations, but because a number of roads crossed there. In the eighteenth century, Vauxhall Gardens was famous – if not infamous – as a centre of fashionable (and low) life. The Gardens, a hundred yards or so from the site of Vauxhall Cross, were well known not only as sources of illicit pleasure and excess, but for their formal avenues and elegant pavilions and follies. (Lacks Dock, east of the Vauxhall Cross site, was the destination for visitors' boats.) The Gardens were swept away in the 1850s. From being a playground, Vauxhall became a workshop. The industries that had existed there from the seventeenth century expanded and diversified: the Doulton pottery was close by, along with forges and glassworks. The site of Vauxhall Cross was for a time occupied partly by a glass factory, then by a vinegar works

Top left: Alban Gate, the "air rights" building on London Wall, completed in 1992. The first in a trio of major London office buildings designed by Terry Farrell and Company

Centre left: Farrell's Embankment Place is constructed above Charing Cross railway station; the striking arched roof is a prominent landmark on the river

Bottom left: Vauxhall Cross completes the trio of commercial developments designed by the practice during the 1980s - a testimony to Farrell's positive contribution to London

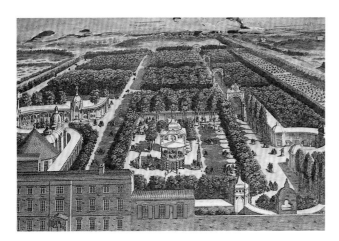

Right: In the 18th century Vauxhall Gardens was famous as a centre of fashionable - and low - life

and gin distillery. During the early 1930s the distillery closed and the site was put to use as an oil depot, a noxious use typical of the South Bank.

Even in the late eighteenth century, Vauxhall had a semi-rural character, with fields close at hand. Its under-development was a consequence of poor communications. Only in 1816 was Vauxhall Bridge opened (an earlier "Vauxhall Bridge" had spanned only the little river Effra, now reduced to an underground culvert) and it remained a toll bridge until 1879. The bridge was an early example of iron construction in London, but by the 1890s the old bridge was in a poor state and rebuilding began in 1898. The new bridge swept away a picturesque if squalid collection of old houses and factories, clustered along the river bank.

Yet even the bridge did not greatly change Vauxhall. The London & South Western Railway into Nine Elms (later extended to Waterloo) cut through the area in 1848, confirming its industrial character. Vauxhall shrank even more into the hinterland of London, becoming at best a traffic interchange (especially after the "improvements" of the 1970s).

In 1955 Land Securities acquired the Vauxhall Cross site for development, clearing away the oil storage tanks in the early 1970s. Yet nothing was done with it, despite the building boom of the late 1950s and 1960s and the construction across the Thames of the Millbank Tower, which was one of London's first new highrise office blocks. The land was sold in 1973 to European Ferries for £1 million. But the property market was in recession and

Vauxhall Cross remained undeveloped. In 1980, European Ferries launched plans for a development, one of which was to prove highly contentious.

The "Green Giant" was the work of architects Abbott Howard; it was an office block nearly 500 feet tall looming over the bridge and river, and figuring prominently in views upstream from Westminster. A rash of towers – the Hilton Hotel, Knightsbridge Barracks, the Shell Tower and Centre Point – had changed the look of London and had become the object of critical and popular dislike. Nobody wanted more high buildings, and one on the river close to Parliament (in view of the Members' Terrace) was unlikely to be well received. There was an immediate reaction to the proposal, with local planning policies being invoked in support of a campaign to quash it. The Secretary of the State for the Environment at the time was Michael Heseltine, who called the scheme into a public inquiry and then refused it planning permission. The Green Giant was quickly slain. The Vauxhall Cross site was once more in limbo.

The so-called Effra site next door – across Vauxhall Bridge – was sold by the PSA also in 1980 (for a reputed £4 million). Heseltine ruled that the two sites should be considered together with the aim of achieving some kind of harmony. A competition was suggested for the combined site. European Ferries were not responsive and appointed new architects to draw up an alternative scheme. Lambeth Council had to consider new schemes for the two Vauxhall sites, but the Environment Secretary was determined to

Left: The "Green Giant" designed by Abbott Howard caused a furore when it was unveiled. Visible from the Members' Terrace of the Palace of Westminster, it was refused planning permission by the then Secretary of State for the Environment Michael Heseltine

take a personal hand in their future development. (He had also called in schemes for Coin Street, near Waterloo, St Mary Overie Wharf, Southwark and Mansion House in the City.) Emphasising the importance of the location for the look of London, Heseltine declared that the site was one of the best in all Europe. The property market was in the ascendant again, and there was no reason why a scheme of quality should not be expected. Vauxhall Cross was not to be a backwater forever.

The impasse was broken by a new player in the history of the site, Ronnie Lyon of Arunbridge, who put together a development package for the combined Vauxhall sites. With Lyon's support, Heseltine was able to announce a competition for the site. The Environment Secretary agreed that, if the winning scheme was of proven merit, it would quickly gain planning permission without further delay, arbitrarily bypassing Lambeth Council altogether by means of a Special Development Order (SDO) in Parliament, an exceptional device rarely used except in cases where the national interest was involved. The competition would be in three stages, beginning with an open invitation to British architectural practices to submit ideas. A small selection of these – not more than eight – were to be subsequently shortlisted and their developed proposals exhibited for public comment. The assessors – Richard MacCormac and Sir Hubert Bennett nominated by the Royal Institute of British Architects with representatives of Arunbridge and Lambeth – were then to put forward three for a final choice by the developer. It all sounded straightforward enough, if

clearly intended to sidestep established planning procedures. But the outcome was to produce some outspoken criticisms and to highlight the problems architects faced in reconciling the demands of the property industry with the interests of the community. Many argued that the brief underlying the competition was misguided from the beginning and that it allowed for gross over-development.

At first, however, all went to plan. In February 1982, Arunbridge announced that there had been 128 first-stage entries. Eight were shortlisted, those by De Blacam/Meagher, Sir Frederick Gibberd, Nicholas Lacey and Associates, David J Richmond and Associates, Sebire Allsopp, Michael Twigg Brown Associates, Michael Newberry and Terry Farrell. The rejects included several schemes which hinted at the future shape of British architecture in the Eighties – including a severely Rationalist proposal by Ed Jones and an extraordinary Classical project by Bruce-Dick, Colomb & Tranter. By April, the selected firms had produced proposals for exhibition on the site.

The developer, backed by the Environment Secretary, wanted a very large mass of buildings: well over a million square feet of offices, over 200 flats and 40,000 square feet of retailing. No amount of architectural ingenuity could conceal the sheer scale of the project and there was no lack of commentators to suggest that this was simply old-style comprehensive development under another guise. Simon Jenkins, writing in *The Times*, was one of them. But Jenkins had good words for Farrell's scheme: "he proposes the Baths of Caracalla as redesigned by Palladio." Other critics divided their favours. Meanwhile, local community groups and Lambeth (which had declined the invitation to nominate an assessor) were hostile. The spirited campaigner Lady (Rusheen) Wynne-Jones called the entries "diabolical and almost without exception utterly devoid of any artistic merit." On a second visit, she conceded that two of the schemes were, however, "interesting". On the whole, the Heseltine initiative had turned distinctly sour, but Arunbridge were defiant, selecting a winner – Sebire Allsopp – from the shortlist of three (the others were Lacey and Farrell) in May. (Farrell's scheme, it was felt, had lost favour by placing the flats, rather than the offices, on the prime river frontage.) The choice was, in the end, the developer's and made on strictly commercial criteria, though the three schemes were shown to the Royal Fine Art Commission (RFAC). The Environment Secretary and the RIBA – accused of conniving at a cynical exercise in "buying" planning approval – were put on the defensive. Heseltine, defending the use of an SDO to overrule the local authority, commented: "I will defend this competition against all comers." The RIBA was torn by arguments about its part in the affair – how could anyone be certain, some asked, that Sebire Allsopp's scheme would be built? Lady Wynne-Jones and her informal South Bank Committee went to Pinchin Kellow for an alternative scheme, but also talked to Farrell, proposing that he draw up revised, less dense, proposals. She queried the legality of the SDO and got support in Parliament from members on both sides of

the House. The Prime Minister was asked to declare a three mile radius around the Palace of Westminster as a protected area. When the SDO went through Parliament, a two line whip was needed to ensure its passage. There were bad feelings on all sides and misgivings about the future.

Farrell recalls that his involvement with Vauxhall Cross began when he was telephoned by RIBA President Owen Luder in January 1982, with a plea that he enter the competition. "Nobody's entering." Luder had said (with some exaggeration as it turned out). Farrell knew nothing of Arunbridge and there was only a fortnight to produce an entry, but he decided to become involved. A year earlier, he had been asked by publisher and architectural propagandist Andreas Papadakis to participate in a design exercise on a grand scale with London as the canvas. Of the architects invited to take part – they included Jeremy Dixon, James Gowan and John Outram – only Farrell actually produced a proposal: for the Jubilee Gardens on the South Bank. When Vauxhall Cross came along, he looked at his drawings. "The two sites had a lot in common," says Farrell. Both were on the Thames, on great sweeps of the river with views to and out of them and both were hemmed in to the rear.

Two weeks of intensive work produced a scheme, which duly got into the selected eight. Farrell recalls that the scheme "was not entirely to the client's taste", chiefly because it put housing on the river with office blocks rising behind and looking across the roofs of the housing. Rejecting the windswept spaces of modern movement

**Above right:
The competition
for the site
organised in 1982
by Arunbridge
was won by
architects Sebire
Allsopp. Other
entries included a
Classical design
by Bruce-Dick
Colomb & Tranter
(right) and a
Post Modern
composition by
Ed Jones
(below right).**

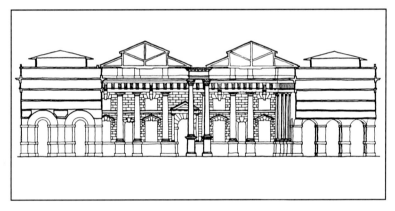

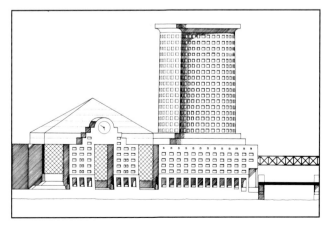

planning that he had identified as destructive of urban form and which survived in some respect in Sebire Allsopp's scheme of zigzagging large blocks, Farrell instead placed his buildings in a tight mesh of streets and courtyards: "parts of a new village". From the north bank of the Thames, the scheme would have read as a layering of differently shaped pavilions, processing formally along the river. Materials would have been a Farrellesque mix: brick, stone dressings, with coloured reflective glass on the office blocks. The scheme was well-received, but failed to win. Backed by Lady Wynne-Jones, Farrell decided to submit his scheme (reduced in scale) to Lambeth for planning permission, feeling perhaps that he had nothing to lose. He had placed his marker on Vauxhall Cross and could hardly be ignored when the future of the site again came up for discussion.

Farrell has never been afraid to chance his arm in the hurly-burly of planning. He was to do the same in the case of Mansion House Square two years later and of developments at Hammersmith and Wimbledon. Having been part of the development process at Vauxhall Cross and seen the Heseltine initiative end in some disarray, Farrell did not simply let the matter drop. The site interested him and mattered to him as a component of London's urban fabric. The Arunbridge competition had produced some interesting proposals, though Farrell felt that the basic idea behind modernist planning, that of large, single-use blocks, had underlain most of them, including the winning entry. He wanted the chance to develop his ideas for the site, producing what he described on its completion, "a very

Farrell's entry to the Arunbridge Competition, with its pavilions set along the bank of the river and change of scale on the Albert Embankment, was reported to be the public's favourite.

complete statement of post modernism" in terms of its urban form rather than its style.

The entire melancholy affair passed into history in summer 1983, when Arunbridge went into liquidation. The sites on either side of the bridge went through a succession of complex ownerships and receiverships. Regalian was in the market for both and bid for them to the current owners, an Arab consortium and (a small part of the site only) Mountleigh, but got only the eastern one. Established by David Goldstone, Regalian's Chairman, in 1972, the company had established a reputation as an innovative and progressive residential developer with a particular interest in urban regeneration schemes. It saw Vauxhall Cross as a potential site for housing and was determined to succeed there where others had failed.

The early 1980s was a period of transition in British architecture and planning. With Mrs Thatcher in power, the property industry began to boom and London, in particular, entered an era of rapid change. The capital had seen it all before – in the 1960s, when London Wall, the Elephant & Castle, Paternoster Square and Park Lane were rebuilt in a fashion that is at odds with London's character and history. Would the same happen again? Heseltine, it seemed, was prepared to back overdevelopment and the RIBA to support him. Architects hastened to get in on the act. The results were disappointing and, some felt, something of a disgrace: a bad augury for the 1980s. Was there no role for the public, let alone for the local authority? The Prince of Wales, it must be remembered, had yet to make the first of his

famous interventions in the field of architecture. But he achieved one significant breakthrough – to make it very hard for developers to ignore public opinion. The collapse of the Arunbridge scheme was a gain for London. It opened the way for a plan that reacts positively to London.

2

Regalian takes

Regalian Properties plc – who were to be Farrell's new client at Vauxhall Cross – had a track record south of the Thames. The company's first major project in London had been Battersea Village, a revamp of an estate of rundown 1930s council flats, converted to 300 luxury flats. This was followed by further regeneration schemes of former council housing at Clapham Junction (The Falcons, a previously intractable group of 1960s high rises), Silver Walk, Rotherhithe and outside London at Washington, near Sunderland, Salford, and in the Midlands and North generally. By 1984 Regalian was in an expansive mood and looking for opportunities especially along the Thames; the river was seen as a continuing theme in their developments. "We were trying to create urban environments in London that actually worked and beyond that we were trying to create communities," says David Goldstone.

The twin planks of Regalian's success were the conversion of existing buildings and residential development. Vauxhall Cross was to take them further into the commercial field with a striking new building. Goldstone and his son Lee (who entered the firm in 1981) had taken a close look at the riverside in the search for suitable development sites. The vacant land at Vauxhall – then in mixed ownership – had obvious appeal. In the event, Regalian was able to acquire only the land east of the bridge (from United Gulf Bank of Bahrain and Mountleigh, who continued to own the Effra site). To some, however, even this seemed risky, given its previous history. The

Left: The Falcons, Clapham Junction, a depressing 1960s high rise estate successfully converted to up market apartments. Below: Battersea Village - Regalian Properties' first major project in London.

Goldstones knew that they faced a difficult planning situation and a likely planning inquiry. Heseltine's SDO (still in force) had provided for an office-based scheme and Lambeth Council's approach was, at best, unpredictable.

The best course seemed to be to arrange a new competition, which was recommended by the RFAC, to whom Regalian (who had never run a competition) had turned for advice as soon as they acquired the site. Amongst the judges was Ted Hollamby, formerly Lambeth's chief planner, who had drawn up the last planning brief for the site in 1982. In contrast to the previous competition – something of a free-for-all and, in the event, a failure – Regalian invited entries from only six practices. Three of them were the finalists from the Arunbridge competition: Sebire Allsopp (the previous winners), Nicholas Lacey (who had built the Crown Reach housing just across Vauxhall Bridge), and Farrell. The others were Conran Roche (a recent spin-off from Fred Roche's department at Milton Keynes and working on Butler's Wharf, Rotherhithe for Terence Conran), Campbell, Zogolovitch, Wilkinson & Gough (a bright young practice which was to do a great deal of work in Docklands) and Architech.

In October 1986, the competitors were asked to produce designs for 250 flats and given a month to do so. In December, the submissions were shown to the RFAC. The Commission backed Regalian's plans for housing (which had provoked opposition from a local authority wary of more "homes for yuppies" and anxious to secure the higher rates income from offices), but found the schemes disappointing.

However, it was positive about Farrell's entry, which could, it commented, "set a new standard for the area." The Commission felt that the bulk and density of the scheme needed further consideration, but its support was a great fillip for Regalian. In January 1987, Regalian commissioned Farrell to progress the scheme.

The Commission was opportune for Farrell. He had won Alban Gate from MEPC at the end of 1985 and Embankment Place, Charing Cross from Greycoat soon after. But by the end of 1986, both these schemes were temporarily on hold. With an expanded staff brought in for the two big projects, Farrell now needed a substantial commission. "I dug out my old scheme," he says, "the only one of the three who did." But Regalian's change from offices to housing meant major revisions. The basic principles remained the same: a family of buildings, an urban village, creating a sense of place in a bleak area, colonising the South Bank. There would be a layered mix of low (four storey) and high rise (a maximum of fifteen storeys) as before, with river views from almost all the dwellings. Flats were easier than offices to mould into interesting architectural forms and the scheme recalled traditional London squares and crescents. But the aim was to avoid a cliff-like impression, with the buildings rising in stages from the river to a great defensive wall (as it were) facing the tides of traffic to the rear. The scheme would be penetrated by a network of pedestrian routes, with car parking at the rear. Materials were much as before: stone and brick with reflective glass and metal. The impression

24

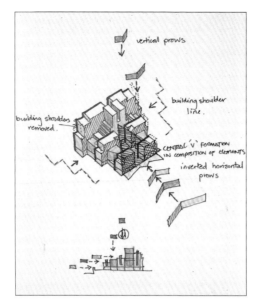

Labels on image 1:
vertical prows
building shoulder line.
building shoulders removed.
CENTRAL 'V' FORMATION IN COMPOSITION OF ELEMENTS
inverted horizontal prows

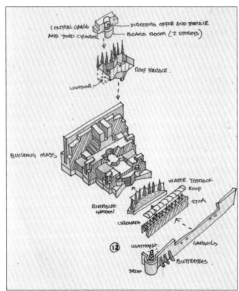

Labels on image 2:
CENTRAL CABLE AND THIRD CYLINDER
DIRECTORS OFFICE AND TERRACE
BOARD ROOM (2 STOREYS)
ROOF TERRACE.
LIGHTWELL
BUILDING MASS
WATER TERRACE
ROOF
STOA
RIVERSIDE GARDEN
COLONADE
LIGHTHOUSE
GARGOILS
DRUM
BUTTRESSES

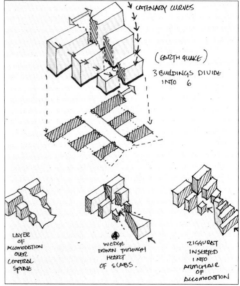

Labels on image 3:
CATENARY CURVES
(EARTH QUAKE)
3 BUILDINGS DIVIDE INTO 6
LAYER OF ACCOMODATION OVER CENTRAL SPINE
WEDGE DRIVEN THROUGH HEART OF SLABS.
ZIGGURAT INSERTED INTO ARMCHAIR OF ACCOMODATION

Right: Axonometric drawing of the 1986 housing scheme for 250 flats.

Left: Farrell's sketches illustrating the development of the design for an office building on the site. The separate pavilions of the housing proposals have disappeared but the change of scale from river front to Albert Embankment remains.

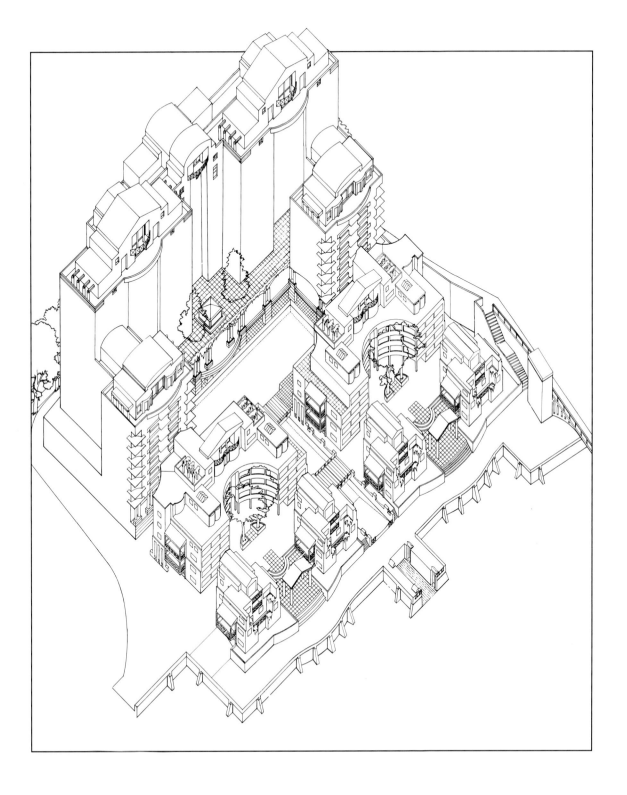

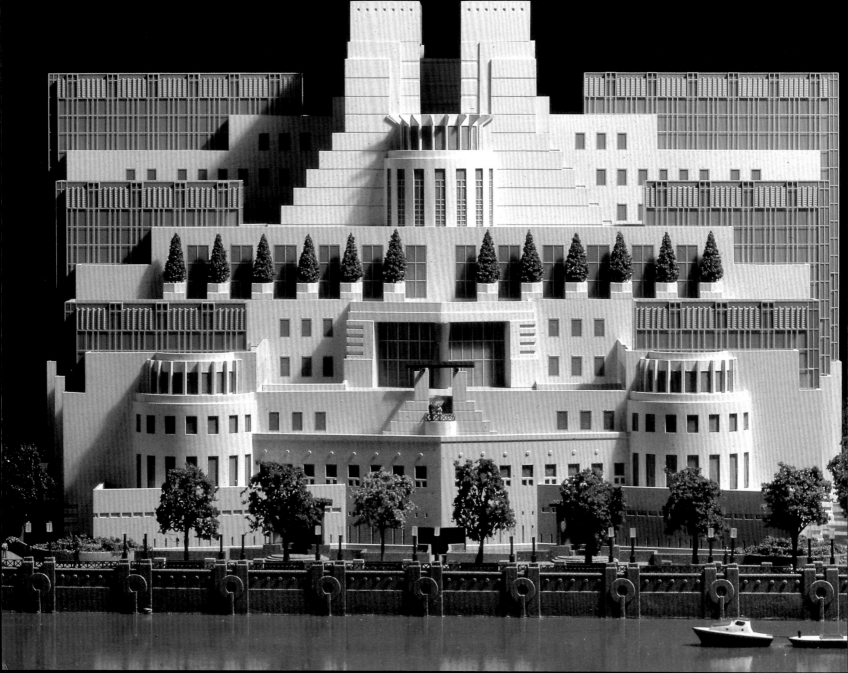

Left: Model of the final design; the completed building varied very little.

from the north bank was to be relatively formal: to some degree, like Embankment Place, a "palace on the river" was the aim. The river would itself invade the site, with a small dock for mooring boats. There would be shopping in a glazed arcade running east/west across the site: shopping, water and boats were the key elements.

Farrell has always been cautious of the label "post modernist". Post modernism, he insists, if it means anything, is not about style, but about ways of building cities. "Simplistic modernism," he says, "is concerned with making objects, rather than urban form and the variety of traditional cities." Modernists, he believes, are too concerned with "light" and "air", which can mean glare and gusts of wind on exposed piazzas. At Vauxhall Cross, Farrell had the opportunity to apply his ideas on a totally cleared site, in contrast to the confined surroundings of Alban Gate and Embankment Place.

In November 1986, Regalian had put in an outline planning application for residential use on the site. Lambeth's attitude was predictable, though its response was not speedy. By February of the following year it was clear that planning permission would not be given. Regalian decided to go to appeal and began to muster support. The RFAC, which had been favourable to Farrell's proposals, was one obvious ally. Farrell went to the Commission's offices in April and presented his developed scheme. He had written to the RFAC Secretary, Sherban Cantacuzino, pleading the case for an extra floor on top of the central block as there would be no gain in space but a good deal in

architectural effect. The issue of height had again been highlighted at this time by an application for the adjacent site by a Dutch developer with the American architects Perkins & Will. Dubbed Tycoon Towers, the proposed blocks on this site would have been 23 storeys high. The Department of the Environment called in the application. Cantacuzino endorsed Farrell's view.

In April 1987, a detailed planning application was submitted for a development now estimated at £36 million. It was to form the agenda for the public inquiry. Farrell's scheme had emerged as a beefy, demonstrative, forceful piece of 1980s architecture, with the rather nervous dialogue between solid and void, masonry and glass, resolved in favour of a solidity reminiscent of the American post modernist Michael Graves. Regalian had by this time brought in Sir Frank Layfield, a leading planning barrister, and a range of consultants, including the late Francis Tibbalds, architect, planner and urbanist and a close collaborator of Farrell on a number of occasions. Ove Arup & Partners had been appointed as structural and services engineers and Cyril Sweett & Partners as quantity surveyors. Wind studies of the proposed building were run. Landscaping and traffic consultants were engaged. The team was coming together.

The inquiry was scheduled for August. Regalian had one major public amenity to offer: a riverside walkway. In addition, it was proposed to create a small boating facility at Lacks Dock, on the eastern edge of the site. Community groups had to be consulted: the lessons of the Arunbridge fiasco had been learned. Lambeth's line at the inquiry became clear. It was not against housing per se, but wanted low-cost, rented units as part of a mix of uses. There was a straight clash of ideologies: the free market as favoured by the Thatcher administration versus Lambeth's attachment to subsidised housing. The conflict saddened Regalian's chairman David Goldstone, whose support for the Labour Party has always been unflinching. But there would be no government funding for public housing. Regalian and its team sailed into battle.

There was no guarantee of government approval. By the end of 1987, with the appeal on the desk of the Environment Secretary (by then Nicholas Ridley), Regalian was looking at the possibility of switching courses to an office scheme. Even then, the coming collapse of the housing market was in the wind, though few realised it. Regalian asked Farrell and the other consultants for their views. Offices, they were told, were a good option, assuming that planning permission could be obtained.

In fact, as early as July 1987, Regalian had been approached by the agents, Savills, on behalf of the government's Property Services Agency (PSA) which was looking at sites around Westminster for new government offices and had shown "a serious expression of preliminary interest" in Vauxhall Cross.

In February 1988, the result of the appeal was made known. The inquiry inspector echoed the RFAC's view that the residential scheme would "set a new standard for the area" and should be approved. The scheme, the inspector

reported, "would create a noteworthy feature of attraction and interest with a fascinating sculptured silhouette as the buildings rise, one on another from the river." Farrell's designs were praised. Regalian announced that they were to go ahead and complete the development in 1991. But the scheme was never built.

This was a period of transition, with the housing boom of the 1980s beginning to show faint but ominous signs of collapse. During 1988 Regalian had strengthened its position on the commercial property scene, with the remarkable financial success of two developments on the Thames at Bankside: Horseshoe Court, which was pre-sold to the Financial Times and Red Lion Court, pre-let to Lloyd's Bank. The company was also becoming involved in joint venture collaborations: with Olympia & York at Heron Quays in Docklands, and Hyperion Properties/Higgs and Hill at Bishopsbridge in Paddington.

During the same month that saw the appeal result announced, Regalian began talks with Lambeth about the possibility of office use on the site. (An outline planning application went to the Council in June and was approved in November.) The residential option remained open. How was the scheme to be adapted for offices, was it just a matter of revising the plans? Regalian's team was being led by their design director, architect Alison Paterson, who put a high emphasis on design quality. Gradually, the brief for an office scheme emerged. For Farrell, this was a difficult time, since two schemes for the same site had, in effect, to be prepared simultaneously by two teams in the office. Only in the autumn did the PSA firm up its interest, following a provisional agreement in May to buy the freehold of a new building.

At first, speculative offices had been the objective. Office development was booming and there was even felt to be a market in Vauxhall (which has the advantage of a tube link from the West End). Regalian's speculative scheme laid down the outlines of an office building, based on a 15 metre grid. But in December 1988, the DoE, as the government ministry responsible for property, signed an agreement to buy the completed building. The process of getting detailed planning permission was already in train. The PSA, the new management group for government buildings, were brought into the discussions by Regalian to talk about the special needs of the prospective occupants. Central government had a poor record where architectural quality was concerned: would the essence of the scheme survive a government take-over?

The existing planning permission provided for a residential development of 406,838 square feet (gross), with parking, riverside walkway and new riverside wall. With a government department as final occupier, the application for offices was developed. PSA looked favourably at the idea of buying a developer's building, with its inherent commercial restraints, rather than a custom-made scheme. Roland King, development director of Regalian, says: "it was like buying an off-the-peg suit, with alterations, rather than a Savile Row job." Though there had been much critical comment about the standards of public

architecture – the DoE's Marsham Street headquarters was often cited as an example of government building at its worst – the budget for Vauxhall Cross would be subject to strict cost guidelines. The final scheme, as built, evolved from that shown in an exhibition on site at the end of 1988. Community groups were brought in for their comments. The response of the Vauxhall Cross Amenity Trust was typical: "we do not want the site to remain empty and blighted for the next twenty years." Outright opposition to development was absent. Even Lambeth Council seemed to be positive – perhaps offices seemed preferable to the luxury housing it had fought against. On Christmas Eve 1988, the PSA signed a deal with Regalian to purchase a completed office block that would be admirably adapted to their specification. The idea of a pre-sale, as at Horseshoe Court, Bankside, was attractive to Regalian, but implied a new level of cost control; there was no element, as is customary in the speculative field, of a "developer's inflation" margin during construction. A sale price had to accurately reflect future building costs with the details of the final office scheme relatively undeveloped.

3

Developing the design

32

Regalian's initial decision in 1988 to pursue an office development as well as housing at Vauxhall Cross reflected widespread uncertainty about the property market, but had been prompted by the serious interest of an end user for offices on the site. Farrell and Sweett had to maintain two distinct teams on the Vauxhall Cross job for the best part of a year (overseen by Regalian with Paterson at the helm). Indeed, in Farrell's office there were briefly three teams at work, as the "occupier" scheme emerged late in 1988 and the speculative office and residential schemes had not been finally abandoned.

Heseltine's controversial SDO, dating back six years, had failed to produce a building on the site, but remained very much in force, permitting the construction of Sebire Allsopp's 1982 office development. However, it related not only to the land owned by Regalian, but to the Effra site too and clearly could not be taken up.

Ironically, the floor areas for Vauxhall Cross were to be dictated by Sebire Allsopp's scheme. Farrell looked carefully at the form of the Sebire Allsopp proposals, but wanted a very different sort of building. No longer could old plans simply be dug out and revised. A new start was required. The idea of a village of small blocks was hardly relevant to the 1980s concept of office space – large floor plates and linear configurations. There was a cool logic behind the proposed plan, designed on a 15 metre grid for a number of tenants and to be built to "shell and core" standard.

Commercial architecture in Britain had undergone radical changes in the 1980s, with the Big Bang of 1986 creating a

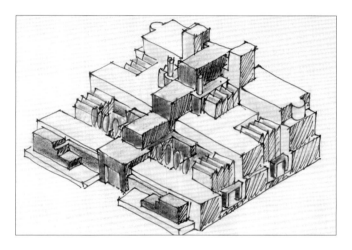

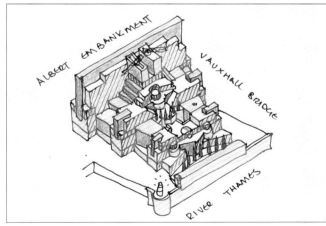

Left: The Farrell design team juggled with a grid of solids and voids to bring daylight into the building

Right: The reduction of the concept of a "village" to a single building markedly reduced the height of the scheme.

Below right: Two of the many models produced in the Farrell office to study the massing of the development.

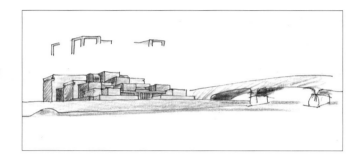

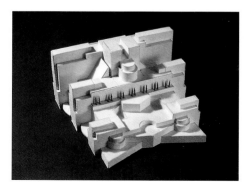

demand – temporary but marked – for very large floor plates designed with dealing rooms in mind. Fast track construction, based on steel frames, had been used by the most successful commercial developers, such as Rosehaugh Stanhope at Broadgate in the City. Mike Glover and Julian Olley of Arup confirm that Vauxhall Cross was designed around a concrete frame from the start: "Alban Gate and Embankment Place were steel because they span space. Steel didn't make sense at Vauxhall." (In fact, the conventional wisdom of the time favoured steel as a more up to date material, but had been shaken by uncertainties about supply, which had delayed Alban Gate along with many other large schemes.) Another early decision was to use fan coils for heating and air conditioning rather than variable air volume systems (VAV) with its requirement for large ducts. These two decisions were to have a significant effect on the basic form of the building.

Numerous study models were prepared at Farrell's office as part of work on the speculative office scheme. They show how Farrell and his team tackled the issue of massing, juggling with overall form in the context of the gric of solids and voids: the atria and courtyards were part of a strategy of daylighting on a tight site. This produced a portcullis-like criss-cross of core and daylit atrium, solid and void. But the massing retained the Farrellesque drama of the residential scheme, with the building rising in layers from the river and incorporating gardens and greenhouses to soften its severity; a green, South London look. The reduction of a "village" to a single building cut the overall height of the scheme markedly. A groundscraper rather than a skyscraper was in prospect.

Farrell sees a memory of the hanging gardens of the Georgian Vauxhall Gardens in the trees and planting of Vauxhall Cross. They mitigate the impact of the architecture, which is not fanciful or light, but serious and even severe. Farrell speaks of the sources of the architecture: 1930s Britain, notably the office block which replaced the Adams' Adelphi; Battersea and Bankside power stations (both by Sir Giles Gilbert Scott, a hero of Farrell's and suggesting the use of brick as a facing material); Mayan and Aztec temples; Manhattan. Farrell loves inter-war architecture, especially that in the Deco tradition, but much of it is essentially graphic and two-dimensional such as the famous Hoover Building. Vauxhall Cross is strongly modelled, foursquare, a freestanding monument, anything but an "outside-in" building. But the architects of the 1930s understood decoration and the way it should be used as an adornment to modern construction. This is an art Farrell seeks to revive. Vauxhall Cross is, he says, an unashamedly "enriched and decorative building." Inter-war designers were equally adept at contrasting traditional materials, including stone and brick, with large areas of glass and steel. This contrast is central to the character of Vauxhall Cross.

Farrell's initial instinct was to use Portland stone (a very costly choice, soon dropped) as a typical London material, cool and clean. Brick was possible, but the choice was, in the end, a form of concrete cladding. "Portland stone is not,

Left: The Adelphi building with its Moderne styling and applied decoration provides a rich source of inspiration, as does Sir Giles Gilbert Scott's Battersea Power Station (right). The Hoover Building in Perivale (below).

anyway, a South Bank colour," says Farrell. "I wanted something warm...". But did concrete mean the streaky-grey look that Farrell deplored at the South Bank arts centre? He went to look at the work of the Catalan architect Ricardo Bofill around Paris and in Montpellier and came away convinced that the material could be dignified and attractive.

Farrell does not see his work as being divided chronologically by stylistic taste. The buildings he designed during his long partnership with Nicholas Grimshaw demanded the same close attention to organisation and detail. Style is not, for Farrell, a veneer, but arises out of building form. "Ignoring the issue of style and taste (which is an obsession in Britain), this is the most competent of my three major London buildings. It is done with such gusto, you can, I hope, put aside your prejudices." The predominant look of Vauxhall Cross is one of honeyish cladding and green glass, the latter at Farrell's insistence against the advice of some of his team, with glass "fins" rising out of the mass. "It is a building with a front, a back and sides," says Farrell, "each designed to address a specific location."

By autumn 1988, the interest of the PSA was becoming more definite. The future occupiers, it was clear, had distinct requirements not catered for by a standard shell and core block and it was decided to develop the building design to meet their needs. Regalian's speculative office scheme maximised floor areas (437,363 square feet gross with 332,767 nett lettable) and was costed at £54 million. Here was a good point of departure for the discussions that the PSA, as project managers, began with the design team late in 1988. Initial comments on the speculative scheme highlighted some necessary changes: the occupier wanted cellular offices rather than open plan space, which resulted in a change of grid from 15 metres to 12, and a 6 metre stand-off zone around the block (a necessity in new government offices), which reduced the size of the floor plate. Inside, there were to be a number of spaces with very specific uses tailored to the occupants' needs. These included sports hall, computer rooms, library, restaurant, covered parking and archive stores. (The more complex aspects of the user requirements were to be met in a second, fit-out phase of works.) More study models for the occupier scheme were made as the brief became clearer and by November the designs were finalised and a detailed planning application submitted providing for the requirements of the specific user. Vauxhall Cross as built is clearly to be seen in these designs. The occupier scheme was slimmer and better proportioned than the speculative scheme, with an extra floor and a clearly delineated form that preserved Farrell's notion of glasshouses and gardens.

The consultation process produced a positive response after a public exhibition of the plans for an office building on site late in 1988. Farrell and Arup moved to detailed design drawings, with the scheme going to the RFAC yet again. The Commission warmly welcomed the scheme as "the best solution so far proposed for this site." Their only concerns related to the colour of the glazing and the proposal to set a line of yew trees at fifth floor level – could trees possibly survive there, it asked? (Farrell was convinced they could and went to great lengths to prove it.)

The confirmation of the pre-sale – claimed as the largest ever – finally sealed the future of Vauxhall Cross. The project was a major challenge even for a developer of Regalian's standing. The company issued a press release in February 1989, stating that the building had been sold for around £130 million (with profit accruing over four financial years) and that construction work was expected to start within a year and take three years. The building now had to be built to a strict cost plan. Regalian brought in two professionals to manage the project. Roland King, development director of Regalian since 1986, realised that completing such a project to time and cost would require a highly experienced project manager and recruited Dick Woods, a civil engineer with extensive project management experience. King and Woods had to immediately look at the consequences of the changes from speculative to occupier scheme before the project went to tender – these amounted to over 4,200 items – and at the evolution of a programme. The underlying rationale was that construction would only start when designs were finalised. For Farrell, this was something new: at Alban Gate and Embankment Place, the designs changed significantly as work progressed on site.

With the financial deal now settled, Regalian had to ensure value for money and established a system of checks and balances before a building contractor had been appointed. They appointed Bovis to carry out an independent value engineering exercise on the designs to confirm costings, programme and buildability. Bovis's report confirmed that they were on course. Cyril Sweett & Partners were brought in to oversee Farrell's production of tender drawings: a difficult relationship on both sides. Initial discussions were held by Sweett with John Laing Construction who commented on the programme and tender process. Significantly, a model of the scheme was commissioned, a symbol of the effective completion of the concept design process.

The whole nature of the project now changed: the building had to be built to agreed designs and to a final cost plan, with everything (and everybody) on a strict programme. Two deadlines were set for the designs: May for exteriors, July for interiors, with the client's final requirements now known. It became clear that security arrangements (now general in many buildings, including airports) would need to be taken into account. The result was an enhanced loading on the building. Its structure and final appearance were inevitably affected.

Arup's engineers began work in February 1989, on site investigation, with bore holes dug into the London clay. The cost plan had already suffered from an underestimate on enabling works, including piling costs and an error in the calculation of the concrete needed. Savings had to be made elsewhere to recoup £1.1 million, but these were possible and, indeed, form part of the cost control programme in any large project where there are certain to be unpredictable elements and adjustments have to be made. This process is central to the work of the quantity surveyor. Arup advised Regalian that the probing and clearing of obstructions for every piling position should be part of the enabling contract as this would expedite progress on construction. The land was quite badly contaminated close to ground level, but this posed no special problem because of the process of sifting, sorting and crushing the soil and stone on site with much of the material being used in the river wall. Proximity to the river produced no particular headaches. As with other sites in London, archaeologists from the Museum of London were anxious to take advantage of impending development to carry out their own investigations (which were sponsored by Regalian). Georgian pottery kilns had already been unearthed on the site. The remains of seventeenth century glass kilns, three bargehouses (for the ceremonial barges of the Fishmongers', Mercers' and Clothmakers' companies) and an inn ("The Vine") now came to light and there was evidence of a river wall. Sealing in the site with a new river wall was part of the enabling works contract, tendered in May and awarded to Fairclough Civil Engineering (who began work in July as the archaeologists moved out). The new wall involved reclaiming 30 feet of land from the river, the occasion of some dispute with the local authority. (This stretch of the river has, in fact, been embanked four times: first in the 1470s, when there was a stone wharf for Westminster Abbey there.)

A new riverside walkway was always a projected public gain in the scheme. The Thames Embankment, that great

Top and far left: Regalian funded archaeological excavations by the Museum of London which discovered 17th century glass kilns, bargehouses, an inn and a river wall.

Below left: The mooring rings with lions' head medallions are an adaptation of a Victorian design used near Lambeth Bridge.

Victorian achievement, hardly extended to the South Bank. Since the war, walkways have been laid out along stretches of the south side of the river, for example, around the Royal Festival Hall and South Bank Centre. But much of the river is still cut off from view and inaccessible. Farrell saw the river walk as part of an overall exercise in urban design, an extended plinth for the building. The design of the river wall is unashamedly architectural, with mooring rings set in large medallions ornamented with lions' heads, an adaptation of a Victorian design seen further down the river near Lambeth Bridge. Farrell used a dark concrete aggregate with a rough finish for the precast panels. (Lambeth Council had been very concerned about the exact colour and texture.) The river wall was part of Fairclough's work on site in the summer of 1989.

As the site was prepared, Farrell's project team, along with Arup, were engaged on detailed designs and intensive meetings, which now included the future occupier's project manager, PSA. Toby Bridge had been appointed at the beginning of the year to run the project for Farrell. Bridge is one of Farrell's most adept lieutenants, with a reputation for painstaking attention to detail in a building project. Another of Farrell's best architects, Steve Brown saw the tricky process of detailed design through from this stage on, working closely with Alistair Guthrie from Arup.

As a government building, Vauxhall Cross was subject to rather different security requirements to those prevailing in the commercial sector. It was also to be a new-style government building. The PSA was responsible for purchasing the building. The price was agreed as was the concept. Regalian had to complete the building to cost if it was to make any profit from the project, but there were no attempts to cut corners or compromise on quality. Vauxhall Cross was always seen as a building of which its developer, purchaser, and users could be proud. In any case, there was nothing to be gained by trying to deviate from the planning permissions given – except delays and added costs. The one exception was the rear (south) elevation, facing the Vauxhall traffic interchange, which had echoed the river elevation but was redesigned at Farrell's suggestion to produce a striking prow towards the road instead of a rotunda. The elevation as completed provides a strongly vertical, rather Deco-ish, gesture towards the south. The redesign also conveniently increased the floor area and affected savings. Lambeth Council was persuaded to vary the consent with the help of the RFAC. The latter body was consulted again on materials for the project and expressed some concern about the character of the glazing, which, it feared, might appear "opaque and uninviting," as it did in a number of recently completed London buildings. This led to further work by Farrell and Arup aimed at avoiding this effect: the glass eventually used was only lightly tinted with a low reflective surface. The team operation was now working as the final designs for the building emerged.

Right: The striking "prow" of the building providing a strongly vertical - rather Deco-ish gesture to the south

4

Managing the team

By July 1989, Vauxhall Cross had been designed and sold, but had now to be built. The architects and engineers had to produce a large number of working drawings and specifications suitable for tendering. There was a great deal of discussion with Regalian as to the form of contract and the programme for construction. The aim was to start on site in April 1990.

There were, however, important issues still to be resolved: the exact character of the cladding and its interface with the structure, the curtain walling, and the mechanical and electrical services, all arising from the detailed requirements of the purchaser. The team were recommending the traditional form of building contract – JCT 80 Lump Sum – whereby a contractor is selected on the basis of tender pricing of Bills of Quantities. The contractor effectively offers a lump sum price for carrying out the works with any variations remeasured. The architect is the leader of the team and has overall responsibility for administering the contract. The disadvantage with this method is that very detailed preparation is needed if costs are to be strictly controlled, as was absolutely necessary at Vauxhall Cross.

Regalian were tending towards the construction management approach, whereby they organised the construction work in-house and went out to tender to different contractors for the various packages of work involved. The contractors are, in this system, employed directly by the developer. Construction management is flexible and can produce a close and harmonious working relationship as the construction manager, usually a contractor, is seen in a non-adversarial professional position. This system, however, places the burden of direct risk on the developer who, in the case of a large project like Vauxhall Cross, must also maintain a sizeable management team.

The general feeling in the development team was to go for the JCT 80 Lump Sum contract, but this did not reflect the need to work further with a selected contractor on finalising the cladding, curtain walling and mechanical and electrical designs. This would require either nomination of specific package contractors – not a favoured route – or a two stage tender process, with an early start on site and detailed matters set aside for stage two. Eventually this was the route proposed by the consultant team. However, Regalian were not convinced that, in the then overheated market place, a two stage tender would provide adequate cost out-turn certainty. Regalian favoured a third system of contract: management contracting. Farrell was somewhat reluctant to use this approach. At Alban Gate, his big City project where the designs had not been finalised before a start was made on site, about 300 sub-contractors had to be co-ordinated under the overall management contractor. There were problems in trying to co-ordinate a project that was developing and being redesigned to some extent as construction happened. Regalian resolved, however, that work package tenders would be issued as a limited number of high value works parcels; around twelve or fifteen principal packages in total.

The management contracting route benefits from the early appointment and involvement of a management contractor. The contractor can then be responsible for overseeing the managing and controlling of the design development – a role which Cyril Sweett & Partners had been undertaking up to this point – procuring of parcels to time and budget, ensuring quality, and generally getting the building constructed to the right quality, at the right price, at the right time.

The project team had identified five potential contractors, all highly experienced firms with major projects: Bovis Construction Ltd, Higgs and Hill plc, Laing Management Ltd, Trafalgar House and Wimpey. All had had initial discussions with Regalian when the form of contract was discussed and from this Regalian had accepted the recommendation of a management contracting path. Regalian invited three of these contractors to tender for the management contract, providing only a brief outline of the scheme (elevations, plans, short description and schedule of floor areas), and received back detailed presentations within a fortnight. It was a tight programme, and interviews were held with the three tendering contractors and all members of the design team. The contractors had to tender on the basis of lump sum fees for the majority of the preliminary works, with reimbursable elements, such as craneage, dealt with separately. There was a lump sum fixed fee for the management of the construction and programme. The presentation produced by Laing Management Ltd – the eventual winners – consisted of an impressive 80-page A3 report outlining their appraisal of the project, recommendations on the specialist advice required, proposals on construction methodology and cost control, their proposed team, site logistics and control systems, all within a 29-month building programme. Laing were selected unanimously by a marking system following the interviews and were appointed the day after.

Laing's team was led initially by Brian Zelly, joint managing director, with Paul Boddam-Whetham as project director. Boddam-Whetham was a civil engineer by training who moved into the contracting business. He had joined Laing Management earlier in 1989. Simon Harding, project manager, came to the project at the beginning of 1990 after a great deal of experience in site management. He had been involved with a number of big London schemes, including Hay's Galleria and the Barker's rebuilding in Kensington, over his 25 years with Laing. He had never before had the luxury of a totally cleared site. Boddam-Whetham and Harding were to be on the project full time for the next three years, along with over fifteen other professionals from the firm.

The development industry boomed in the 1980s and the results are everywhere to see. What the layman does not see is the complex background of both administration and too often litigation, which underlies the process of construction. Project teams can spend a year or two after a building is completed dealing with claims and other legal matters. Management contracting emerged as a result of client dissatisfaction with an industry whose methods of

**Left: Taking shape
- the view across
the river, April
1991**

**Right: Aerial view
of the site, July
1991**

**Far right: The
cladding goes on -
September 1991**

procuring were based on contracts that introduced conflict, the division of responsibilities, lack of adequate consultation between the various sub-contractors, rising costs and too easy resort to the law to sort out disagreements. Roland King of Regalian says: "an architect today sits with a lawyer at one shoulder and an accountant at the other... underneath every management contractor is a lump sum contractor trying to keep his mouth shut." King also believes that new building technologies have outpaced architects' management abilities. A good management contractor is a team leader and communicator keeping his team together to produce the results the client wants.

While the management contractor was being appointed for the £80 million contract coming in September, Farrell and Arup were drawing up lists of potential contractors for the main packages and had made several visits to precast cladding and curtain wall manufacturers throughout Europe and beyond. The cladding element was the largest of its kind yet seen in Britain and it was necessary to appoint a contractor and work with the chosen firm on carrying forward detailed designs. The appointment of Laing as management contractor eased this route. Tender drawings were issued in November 1989. Drawings had also to be prepared for the basic frame that would be constructed on site first. Regalian aimed at awarding 60-70 per cent of the tenders for packages before work began on site in order to secure confirmation of the cost estimate. Farrell had a team of around 40 out of a total office staff of 175 working on Vauxhall Cross preparing tender drawings and performance specifications. Laing's aim was to go out to tender before the end of 1989, on site establishment parcels, initial drainage and temporary power supply and craneage. There was also a need to secure the cladding and curtain walling package contractors. This put considerable pressure on the design team, which spent six weeks working solely on the last two crucial items. Laing's approach was intended to expedite work by means of a strict package procurement programme, nicknamed DORPS (design input, tender out, tender returned, place order, start on site).

The major parcels procurement revolved around cladding and curtain walling particularly because of the necessary design development and the critical interface between those two packages and the concrete frame, which was already in an advanced stage of design by Arup. Cladding, in the event, was awarded to a British contractor, Empire Stone Ltd, the only British firm out of four initially identified for the project. German manufacturers were expected to provide strong competition, but the removal of the Berlin Wall had concentrated their interests on domestic matters. Curtain walling went to a UK subsidiary of the Swiss company Hans Schmidlin (AG) who were working on Norman Foster's airport at Stansted, where Laing were also the management contractors. No British company appeared to be up to the task, but then foreign companies have led in the area of curtain walling for some years. Upon the return of the tenders Schmidlin's was not the lowest, but after considerable investigation it was proposed by the consultant team that Schmidlin were the most competent

Right: Concrete panels are lifted into place, July 1991. A major concern was to ensure consistency of colour throughout the production of the pre cast panels.

At work on site and (below) moulding cladding panels at Empire Stone's Leicester works where the concrete panels were manufactured over a period of fifteen months. Over 2,650 units were cast.

to carry out the task, and had demonstrated a superior understanding of the technical difficulties involved. It was another measure of Regalian's commercial involvement in the detail of the project that they were able to agree to accept a tender that was not the lowest.

The other critical and very complex area for tender – mechanical and electrical services – went out in January 1990, together with the main structural parcel. The mechanical and electrical package was won by the Haden/Phoenix joint venture – created by a union of two leading firms, at Laing's unusual suggestion. The precast cladding, curtain walling and mechanical and electrical parcels accounted for over half the construction costs of the entire 450,000 square feet building. The structure went to Swift Structures Ltd, who also had previous experience of working with Laing.

Regalian's team consisted of Dick Woods and Michael Baxter who were based on site throughout – an early decision and typical of the developer's hands-on approach – to oversee the construction and financial programme. Any large building project relies on effective communication between the various parties, but all too often is burdened by meetings and excessive paperwork as the various professionals, aware of their liabilities, cover their position with letters and memos. Regalian wanted to create an open approach, with problems discussed and resolved informally before anyone resorted to paper. Sub-contractors were encouraged to talk to Laing and Regalian directly where difficulties arose. Rather than deal with claims at a later

stage, with money worries casting a shadow on the project, Regalian chose to settle "entitlements for extras" immediately, recognising that future relationships mattered most. There were monthly principals' meetings from the start with all the consultant team present including the management contractor. These were informal in character, without agenda or minutes. A degree of conflict and confrontation is almost an inherent feature of any construction project. The ability to manage conflict was a strong element in Regalian's philosophy and one that percolated throughout the whole team: "it is the difference between peace-making and peace-keeping," says King.

Another feature of the project, by no means unique amongst the more forward thinking developers, but used to great advantage on this project, was the series of dinners, held at six month intervals, attended by the managing directors of all the principal players in the project. The dinners were co-hosted by Regalian and Laing and not only enabled the package contractors' managing directors to learn first hand from the client what was envisaged and what would be expected from them, but to see as each package was completed that success was in the making. These were also occasions when the managing directors of the participant companies had a chance to meet each other and form new routes of communication that aided the progress of the project.

The idea of a team can be rather artificial, it all depends on the personalities involved. Business relationships sometimes require hard work and communication is always

By early 1992 the quality and complexity of the detailing was apparent. The stepped ziggurat form of the building created no fewer than 60 separate roof areas.

the key. Regalian, with Laing, set up three "team enhancement programmes" throughout the course of the project. At one level, these were occasions held over a couple of days away from the site when people got to know each other better socially. Equally, however, they were intended to improve communications by putting people into scenarios that tested their responses to problems and crises. Everyone involved felt that they were useful and very relevant to the open management approach that prevailed throughout every stage of the project.

The collaboration of Farrell, Arup and Cyril Sweett was helped by the use of an advanced CAD system, an AutoCAD replacing Cadraw, which Arup had used for some fifteen years, with a database at Arup's offices. CAD is now common in architectural practices of any scale, but it was unusual at this time for three professional firms to share a common system. There were teething problems, but once the common language had been agreed, things went smoothly. Schmidlin was also brought into the system in due course. The operating system was updated as the job progressed from MS-DOS to Unix because of the complexity of the drawings and memory requirement. Julian Olley of Arup comments that, as a consequence of the integration of computer systems, there were not only savings within the practices but also for the design development, in spite of the learn as you go methodology.

It was late in 1989 that Fairclough arrived on site at Vauxhall Cross, having been awarded the £1.5 million enabling works contract, with the aim of preparing for the main construction work to begin before Easter. Fairclough's work included the creation of the new river wall embankment, which extended the site, and clearing underground obstructions that had been located by probing pile positions. At the suggestion of Arup, Regalian commissioned a test pile at a cost of £100,000, expenditure more than repaid by subsequent economies in piling.

Laing's first task on site was to establish access and to provide temporary drainage and power. The overall strategy was to construct the building beginning with the corner in the angle of the river bank and bridge and to work outwards from there, floor by floor. Site huts are an inevitable and mundane part of construction, but those at Vauxhall Cross, which housed offices not only for Laing and the design team but also for Regalian, extended to some 60,000 square feet in the form of three storey blocks, considerably larger than is normal in a project of this size. Having representative members of the team on site ensured effective and swift communication.

Piling began two weeks ahead of time before Easter 1990. Arup's recommendation that all 275 piles, up to 32 metres deep, were to be probed in advance led to a smooth contract undertaken by Stent Foundations that was completed in thirteen weeks, a week ahead of schedule. As soon as piling was near completion, Swift Structures moved in. Their task was to build in 48 weeks the substructure and concrete frame of the building. Laing provided through EPL (their own plant hire company, but appointed under competitive bid) four cranes, the tallest 100 metres high with a 50 metre radius, arriving in June 1990. The cranes were to be a regular feature of the Vauxhall Cross skyline for the next eighteen months. The wisdom of the decision to go for a reinforced concrete rather than a steel frame was ever more obvious as the work progressed. "It saved time and trouble," says Harding, "since there was no need for fire proofing." The advantages of concrete were in fact manifold: it is sturdier as a frame, though deflection was a major consideration when it came to applying cladding; it has much better acoustic qualities; it copes well with temperature variations; and, as Farrell says, "gives you form immediately."

The form of the concrete frame reflected the occupier's requirements: six perimeter cores for plant rooms, service risers, escape stairs and toilets, with internal cores for lifts. Four atria rising from the ground floor and two beginning on the second floor enhance the quality of the office spaces. The complex structural grid varies from 4.8 to 9.6 metres with intervals of 1.2 metres, while the typical floor to floor height is 4 metres with ground and first floor 6 metres and 5 metres respectively. However, the principle was to leave large (20 metre square) areas for services rising through the building, to be filled in later as these were designed in detail. This avoided space problems for later contractors. Work at basement level included the provision of fuel tanks east of the building and watertight plant rooms (they were only two inches above the river level and contained a ring of pumped wells at 2 metre intervals around the building). Basement excavation used the open cut method for

economy and ease of access for plant installation. The floor slabs were then cast floor by floor in their entirety, with staircases for easy access, rather than building high and low blocks separately. Each floor was back propped as the next was cast on site. With the completion of the fifth floor, the frame of the building was 80 per cent complete.

Swift's work force built up to a maximum of 190 on site in September 1990. At the height of their activities they were pouring 1,300 cubic metres of in situ concrete a week. Swift were using a new aluminium form work system specially purchased for this project at a capital cost of over £1 million. They also brought on to site a new lorry-mounted concrete pump for placing concrete at a further capital cost of £169,000. Swift completed its phase of the works by March 1991, and by the time the fifth floor was underway, the cladding was being applied lower down the building. Tying in frame and cladding was a crucial design matter. The design details were much more complicated when they emerged than Swift had allowed for. Alterations to the programme had to be made in order to make up time and keep to the already tight programme. Regalian were approached to help resolve the problem. A realistic agreement was reached, providing for Swift's additional costs. A financial settlement, linked to performance targets was agreed without acrimony, since Regalian were anxious to keep the project on programme. This was a test of the management contract approach – passed with flying colours. Nobody ever believes that a concrete frame will be completed on time, this one was.

5

Working contracts

As Vauxhall Cross rose as a new landmark on the Thames, with Swift constructing the frame of the building during 1990 and early 1991, orders were being placed for the remaining parcels of the project. The details of the exterior had been finalised by June 1990 with the appointment of Schmidlin to undertake the curtain walling and Empire Stone for the precast concrete cladding.

Long before the tender stage for the precast cladding was reached, Farrell had conducted detailed discussions and visits with potential suppliers. One of them, Partek Ergon, had even helped prepare the designs for the planning drawings. This Belgian company did not, however, win the contract because it could not meet Laing's programme without using more than one moulding plant. The contract went to the British company, Empire Stone, whose previous jobs had included the hotel at Chelsea Harbour and Quinlan Terry's Richmond Riverside scheme. The success of the pre-cast cladding is a vital element in the overall architectural success of the building. The contract was one of the largest and most demanding ever undertaken for precast cladding in this country. Empire had to work with the architects and engineers to design both panels and fixings in detail. Spanning some 2.4 metres wide and 4 metres high, the panels sit on a "nib" attached to the floor edges. They are attached to structural hard points close to the columns, with sometimes as many as four panels between a pair of columns. Three different structural systems had been used to connect the panels: beam, tied arch and a three pin arch. In a few cases, where the spans are too large, the structure was strengthened. The structural grid varied between 4.8 and 9.6 metres with the increments of 1.2 metres. The cladding system itself expresses the 1.2 x 1.2 metre square grid into which the panels are incorporated. The joints between the panels proved a particular problem. Farrell wanted them to be an architectural feature and aimed at 15mm gaps. Arup's calculations ruled this out because of creep and deflection in the concrete frame and the gap had to be extended to 20mm. Neither was it a matter of simply fixing masses of concrete to the wall. The cladding system had to incorporate vents, insulation and vapour control to counter condensation. Empire was able to cope with all the requirements of the brief, including the vital issue of how the cladding was to be fixed to the structure. Extra steel work had to be inserted to carry the panels where the structure was inadequate. Some 10,000 fixings were required and were drilled into the structural frame. A maximum movement of 2mm at the joints is allowed for.

Vauxhall Cross was to be Empire's largest and most complex commission ever: 60 per cent of its total production over a period of fifteen months. Empire had to prove to the architects that it could meet their demand for a very high degree of colour consistency. It produced 20 test panels, manufactured on different days by different operatives, to show that variation within the material could be kept well within the strict design brief. Farrell's team could not detect the differences.

Manufacturing the panels off site at Empire's

The contract for the precast cladding was one of the largest and most complex ever undertaken in the UK. Their manufacture occupied 60 per cent of Empire Stone's production for fifteen months. The architects demanded a very high degree of colour consistency

62

Leicestershire works began in the autumn of 1990. The panels were made in fibreglass-lined timber moulds with granite slices set in the bottom to give a natural finish. Concrete was then allowed to set in the moulds for eighteen hours and the final acid treatment began after three days. Over 2,650 units were cast, with 1,400 types of panel, meaning the typical mould produced fewer than two casts before it was altered. The fixing of the cladding began in January 1991 as the fifth floor of the frame was being completed by Swift, with the heaviest units being the large panels on the ground floor. Mobile cranes were needed in addition to the four tower cranes on site, as panels were erected directly off the lorries that brought them in. Within three months the cladding was substantially complete after 575 deliveries to site and a total of 9,400 tonnes had been craned into position.

The overall skin of the building, a dynamic mix of pre-cast and glazed curtain walling, had to be co-ordinated with the two elements being installed alongside each other. Schmidlin faced a task as challenging as Empire's: 12,000 square metres of glass and aluminium covering the six perimeter cores and the internal atria. It was a far more complex undertaking than they anticipated and a good working relationship with Empire on the design of interfaces was essential. There were communication difficulties at times as the design tolerances between precast concrete and the engineering discipline of aluminium framed curtain walling had to be made compatible. There was, in addition, the geographical

12,000sq metres of glass and aluminium covering the six perimeter cores and internal atria were installed by Schmidlin

Four distinct window and curtain walling systems and 40 different aluminium profiles were developed specifically for the project

distance between the two companies as well as language and cultural barriers. From experience Schmidlin had learned to take a more strictly contractual attitude than Empire, whose collaboration with Laing was such a success. Production and design were complicated by the special requirements of the purchaser, which resulted in enhanced loadings on the building. Schmidlin described the job as "the toughest package of performance specifications we have ever tackled." They reported that 60,000 design hours went into the production of nearly 5,000 drawings with 1,200 design reviews required by the project team at Farrell's office. The glass may look homogeneous, but 25 different types were required to meet specific requirements in all parts of the building. There were four distinct window and curtain walling systems and seven different colours of powder coated aluminium on 40 different profiles developed specifically for the project. Even the doors and louvres were especially designed, this was a custom made building. Schmidlin began work in May 1991 and they completed 39 weeks later. Their work on site was far more labour intensive than Empire's, a workforce in excess of 100 compared to the 30 fixing operatives for the latter.

A striking feature of Vauxhall Cross is its ziggurat-like stepped form with various elements of the composition dramatically grouped like a great ocean liner with layers of decks rising from the river. The complexity of the design produces no fewer than 60 roof areas, some visible from the street, others tucked away high up. The roofing package was undertaken by Prater Roofing Ltd and work began late in 1990, some time before the cladding work started. The roofs are covered in two layers of conventional felting with insulation on top, a typical Farrell recipe that ensures old fashioned reliability. Visible roofs are paved with gravel perimeters and colour patterned stone slabs. Prater comments, "usually when we arrive at site it is not ready for us, and then we are expected to make up time. At Vauxhall Cross we were brought in when areas were ready and we ensured our programme was adhered to."

Vauxhall Cross is built to last, but any building needs to be maintained. The PSA is exacting in its maintenance requirements for new government buildings, realising that too many public buildings have acquired a shabby, neglected image. Every square inch of Vauxhall Cross is accessible for cleaning and repair, should the need arise, with a £1 million system of mobile cranes, cradles and davits outside, and gantries and cradles in the atria. This maintenance equipment, supplied and installed by Kobi Cradles Ltd, is designed to be unobtrusive when not in use. A specially designed mobile "spider" is available to clean the exteriors of ground and first floors. Concrete staining was an issue that had to be confronted. Tests were carried out and produced the final designs for the cladding panels, which have a 20mm setback stepping up the facade with internal drainage systems at the joints. In addition, the deep window recesses have prow-shaped cills guiding water to the edges and drainage holes that, in turn, lead to internal pipes. In the rotundas, water is let in to precast tubing in the cills. Weathering cannot be avoided, but the attention to design details will ensure that the building's appearance does not change too dramatically.

Appointing contractors, particularly in a recession, is always a testing time. Laing led the procurement process, but all consultants were involved in a combined final report on recommendations to Regalian. All the selected package contractors stayed the course – but then only reliable companies had been approached in the light of worrying failures in the construction industry.

The third major package was for the mechanical and electrical services. The recommendation from the team was again not to accept the lowest tender but to take up the joint venture bid from Haden/Phoenix. During the tender appraisal period Arup was involved in considerably more work on the services design – a consequence of the increasingly complex user requirements. Haden/Phoenix were then asked to review these changes in order that, when the contract was placed, it would represent the actual requirements of the job. This enabled Haden/Phoenix to reassess their bid, ensure they understood what was required, and avoid undue risks.

Fitting complex services into buildings is always difficult, and notorious for increasing costs dramatically, as Cyril Sweett points out. Laing had suggested the joint venture between Haden, for mechanical and public health aspects, and Phoenix, for electrics. Haden/Phoenix was the only sub-contractor with a design team full-time on site (from June 1990), a distinct advantage in the view of Arup. The latter had decided early on that a heating and air conditioning system run by fan coils should be used in preference to the VAV systems popular in speculative office blocks during the 1980s. VAV systems have advantages: no need for water in ceilings, fewer moving parts, less maintenance and smaller power loads. A fan coil system relies on pumping hot and cold water through a building, but requires far smaller areas of pipes and ducting, is cheaper to run and more flexible for a variety of power loads. Even so, the fitting in and organising of 1,200 fan coil units, high and low voltage power systems, 20 km of hot and cold water pipes, 75 km of drainage, chilled water, heating and sprinkler pipes before the cabling, power, and ducts are included, represents a complex task.

The building's symmetrical form helped here. The basement occupies about a third of the foot plate and the six perimeter cores are topped by roof-top glazed areas housing plant rooms. There are two extra cores to the rear, with central cores housing additional services and passenger lifts. Installing the services was a test of Laing's performance. The delivery and installation of piped ductwork cabling and prefabricated service units into a drylined and watertight building is only the beginning. The quality control systems, flushing, filling and testing of the systems, takes far longer and is always prone to some problems.

Haden/Phoenix employed the largest number of men on site for the longest time, overlapping with a majority of the other parcels. This overlap is the route of most difficulties on building projects, "often resulting in claims of up to 50

per cent of tender price," according to Regalian, but this did not happen at Vauxhall Cross. Haden/Phoenix's work on site began with the installation of basement plant chillers, pumps, boilers, transformers switching panels, sprinkler and water storage tanks in January 1991 before the fifth floor of the building had been completed. Arup and Haden/Phoenix had to struggle to fit plant into the roof top rooms without demanding a major redesign of the space and the inevitable delay.

Luckily, the winter of 1990/91 was mild and the cranes were hardly out of action. For two Christmases, Laing offered the use of the site canteen to the Salvation Army, who provided over 500 meals for the homeless there. (A donation from Regalian paid for blankets and other comforts.) Cladding and roofing went ahead smoothly, allowing the building to be made watertight. The seven rooftop plant rooms were temporarily water-proofed as an interim measure to allow craning-in of services and plant. The drylining and joinery contract went to Thermofelt Contracts Ltd and closely followed the finishing works of both the cladding and the installation of the M&E services. The major part of the joinery work consisted of 624 door sets veneered with American white oak.

The eight passenger lifts and goods lift (capacity 5 tonnes, the largest on the market) were supplied by Thyssen Lifts and Escalators Ltd. The delivery and installation of lifts has always been problematic on major construction projects, but the lift industry has sought to make improvements in recent times by careful preprogramming of work. The lift shafts were made available to Thyssen early on in the programme and they remained consistently ahead of schedule up to and including the final load testing of the lifts. The small documents lift was awarded to Linvar Ltd.

The site reached a peak of activity in spring and summer of 1991. The main power came on in May as suspended ceilings were being installed. The suspended ceiling contract was placed with How Lindner plc, a joint venture company between the UK How Engineering Group and Lindner AG. During the process of the contract the joint venture split up and the work was carried out directly by Lindner AG. The ceiling layout is designed to allow squares of 1.2 metres to be removed for cabling requirements against a specially designed (and now patented) rigid frame, the first time this system was used in the UK.

Another common source of delays on large building projects arises from the completion of the toilet and washroom areas. There has been a tendency to use prefabricated off-site toilet pods that are then craned into position within the shell of the building. The layout and particular requirements of Vauxhall Cross precluded the use of prefabricated toilet pods, but there was an early decision based on the concept of a minimum number of works packages that the work in installing both mechanical and electrical services within toilet pods and their wall, ceiling and floor finishes, together with all the cubicles and sanitary ware, should be in one package. This was awarded to A D Davies & Co Ltd, well known for their shop fitting skills.

A brief description of the major elements of a building inevitably skips over a multitude of items that nonetheless are essential. System Floors Ltd installed raised access floors early in 1992, but only in specified computer rooms providing for a 600mm floor void. Metalwork, including that to internal stairs, balustrading and handrails to parapets outside, was provided and installed by Singer & James Ltd.

Vogue Development Company Ltd, who had worked for Regalian before on the prestigious Palace Green residential development, were awarded the general builder's package. Whilst this description conjures up the minor odds and ends of block work and walling and hole drilling necessary within a complex building, the extent of the package amounted to a major building contract, and one requiring total integration with all the other trades.

The yew trees on the fifth floor, one of the most unusual items in the design, were among the last items to be craned into position. They were grown in Italy and acclimatised in Scotland. Four tons of earth were used to plant them in containers with water, feeding and drainage systems built in. They will need trimming once a year and there is every confidence that they will thrive. Siddeley Landscapes Ltd were given the job of ensuring that Farrell's passionate desire to include this element is brought to successful fruition.

The final phase of the work was the laying out of the riverside walk: slate, paving stones, gravel and furnishings create a nascent public space for the South Bank. Plane trees, box hedges, wisteria and lavender begin the process

The yew trees were one of the last items to be craned into position. They were grown in Italy and acclimatised in Scotland and will require trimming once a year.

of humanising it. A gazebo, fountains and a kiosk designed to operate as a cafe, are equally intended to enhance the space and encourage its use. All these external works were awarded to Swift in their second major package on the scheme, so impressive had been their previous work .

The thousand and one moving parts that go into a large building are complex in themselves, but somebody has to make sure that they all work. At Vauxhall Cross, this was the job of commissioning managers Paul Banyard and Associates, who were appointed under a separate package because of their previous work with the PSA. They provided reassurance for the team that all was installed on time and worked by constantly reviewing the programme with the tight schedule in mind.

One of the remarkable features of the Vauxhall Cross project is the way in which it is viewed by those who have been most closely involved: as an effective, indeed cordial collaboration between all the professionals. Seeing a building completed on time and to cost is a satisfying and, sadly, rare experience. The recession undoubtedly helped the team remain largely unchanged throughout and the supply problems for materials and prefabricated components, common during the 1980s boom years, did not occur. Tight and effective management, pre- and post-contract was, however, a major factor in the success story of Vauxhall Cross: a mammoth project completed on schedule and built below budget.

6

Art and technology

In the half-century since the modern planning system was, in effect, invented, the face of London has been transformed. "Built according to the plan," might be the epitaph on many areas of the capital; once varied, humane and full of potential for positive change, now wrecked, desolate and blighted. Fortunately, plans sometimes fail to materialise: human nature, the vagaries of taste, political opportunism, coincidence, the unpredictable operations of "the market" and the workings of fate play a hand.

Such is the case at Vauxhall Cross. The site might have been occupied by the last of London's high-rise office towers, a building that would surely have been reviled even before it was completed, or by a dense housing development. It might have been left empty, like the adjacent Effra site, yet another South Bank wasteland to highlight the sharp divide imposed by the river Thames. In the event, it is the location for one of the most striking and expressive late twentieth century buildings in London.

The building is, firstly, a major work of contemporary architecture. Farrell's buildings express the dialogue between art and technology which, he believes, must be held in balance to produce good architecture. Looking back into relatively recent history – the Arts and Crafts and the eclecticism of the 1930s – Farrell notes that it was not always so. "The scope for a more humane and decorative technology," he writes, "is even greater today."

Architecture, Farrell believes, is constrained by "an overemphasis on utility . . . on architecture as pure art [which] deadens so much of the freedom with which it can be exploited." C R Mackintosh, Raymond Hood, Sir Giles Gilbert Scott and Owen Williams fused art and technology: Farrell seeks to do the same. Vauxhall Cross is the most potent built expression of his philosophy to date.

Secondly, Vauxhall Cross is a singular success for its developers, Regalian; formerly identified overwhelmingly with residential development, but now the progenitors of a state-of-the-art office building that is one of the new sights of London. The circumstances of the project, particularly its pre-sale, and the single-minded commitment with which it was carried through on all sides, helped to carry the initial vision through to fruition. As an example of teamwork, nobody who was involved – management contractors, quantity surveyors, engineers, those responsible for the many "packages" and all the rest included – doubts that Vauxhall Cross was outstanding as an exercise in collaboration.

Lastly, the government, as final client, buyer and user of the building, has brought into question the belief (all too well-founded in the past) that civil service offices are necessarily dull, faceless lumps. Vauxhall Cross is a building that breaks the mould in more ways than one.

The character of the completed building is the outcome of a series of decisions: Farrell's appointment, initially to design a residential scheme, the change to offices (and the pre-sale of the building to a single user), the choice of a concrete frame in preference to steel, and the selection of materials appropriate to the structure and, equally, expressive of a very specific aesthetic.

The Albert Embankment entrance which expresses Farrell's interest in the fusion of art and technology. Vauxhall Cross is the most potent illustration of his philosophy to date.

Left: The fountains, hard landscaping and trees bring back to the area the lively environment of the historic Vauxhall Gardens.
Right: The central column in the prow of the building provides a point of focus within the complex geometry of the facade.
Far right: The yew trees in situ.
Below right: The riverside walk

The full height atrium: the division between solid and void, precast and glazed cladding is a logical expression of the building's concept

The basic form of the building, three parallel blocks rising in height as they step back from the river and linked by glazed courtyards and atria, derives from the original (residential) scheme, which began as a "family" of buildings set in streets and squares. The original concept has been tightened up, condensed to produce a single building, a groundscraper that skilfully packs in a lot of space without dominating the skyline. The key lies in the tight but flexible grid, which admirably provided for the complex needs of the end user. The division between solid and void, precast and glazed cladding, on the exterior of the building is equally logical, reinforcing its division into three stepped blocks and the taut balance between monumentality and lightness which is the essence of the scheme.

If the architectural details evoke the 1930s in places, this is not altogether accidental, given Farrell's admiration for the best work of that era. The south (street) elevation of the building is especially Deco in effect, from its Hoover-ish railings to its jutting, V-shaped prow. The use of dark green granite (from Brazil), in appearance not unlike the Siberian marble popular between the wars, strengthens the impression. From the river, the high level rotunda, flanked by service towers, hovers somewhere between Giles Gilbert Scott buildings and the Rockefeller Center (another Farrell favourite). The inspirations are clear, but the end-product is anything but derivative. The detailing of the precast cladding on the south elevation is formed into chevron moulds below the windows and the louvred units at the base of the building have a similarly streamlined look.

Elsewhere, however, the deep-set windows have a more specifically post modernist character, rationalist in their severity and producing an effect of dignity quite devoid of the vulgarity to which post modernism can descend. The great sweeps of curtain walling rapidly dispel any thoughts that a literal revival of the 1930s style is being attempted. Encasing the service towers, the glazing is part of a concerted attempt to create convincingly sculptural architecture. At Lloyd's, Richard Rogers expressed the service towers as turrets on the building. Farrell integrates them, subordinates them to the total effect: an instance of his belief that technology must not be permitted to dictate architectural form, but be kept within an overall discipline. Farrell's architecture is finite, defined, in a way which high tech architects find disturbing.

Nonetheless, there are elements in Vauxhall Cross of the extreme and the fantastic; nowhere more so than in the determination, in the face of much scepticism and some opposition, to make trees part of the architecture. Whether they are a deliberate memory of the famous Vauxhall Gardens, or just a response to riverside terraces that ought to be pleasant places to walk and talk, is unclear. But they are now vital to the building and great efforts have been made to ensure that they survive.

The ideas behind Vauxhall Cross have survived largely intact into the completed building, but could do so only because of the work of an outstanding engineering team at Arup and a framework of structural and services design that underpinned and strengthened the architectural strategy.

Below: The Albert Embankment facade.

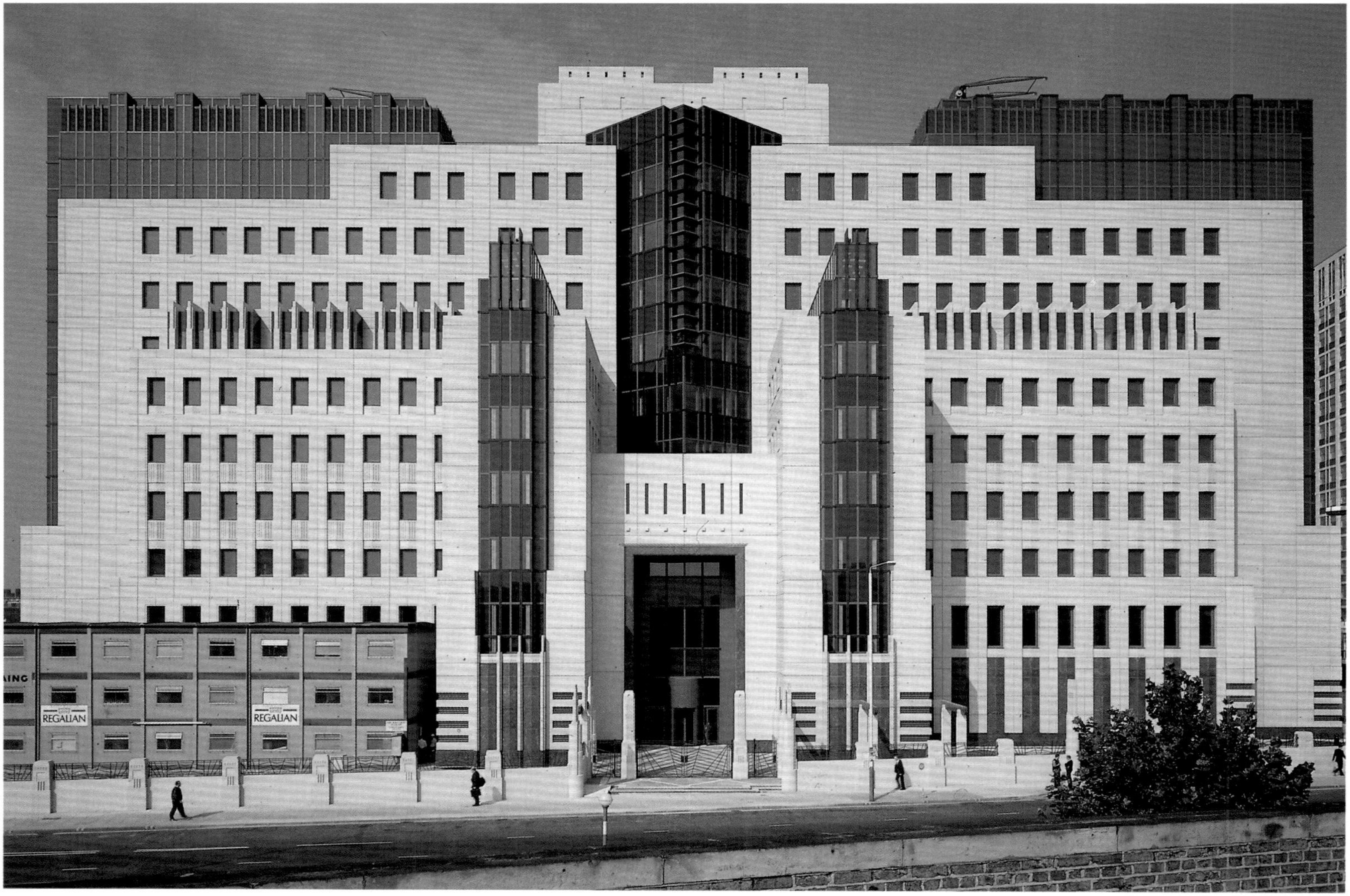

Also, given the particular circumstances of the project, with the building being tailored to the requirements of a purchaser, the contribution of the four principal contractors, two for cladding, one for services, one for structure, was of vital importance. The rightness of the decision to use a management contract for the project was confirmed as the various parcels were developed while construction got underway. Coordinating the two cladding packages was a particularly high priority. Farrell speaks of the "ruthless consistency" of the building: finishes matter. The development of the cladding packages could have posed problems but the end result was certainly to improve the look of the building as well as its performance. At Vauxhall Cross, advanced building technology is not used for mere effect and the leading edge nature of much of the project is too easily forgotten. Empire had certainly done nothing like it before. The size of their design team (which numbered as many as 20) underlines the degree to which the key contractors were involved in the design process. The services contractors, Haden/Phoenix, had a team of over 30 working within parameters laid down by Arup's engineers. Vauxhall Cross is a prime example of the intelligent building of the 1990s, where communications technology is integrated into the design rather than applied later.

Laing Management, under the on-site direction of Boddam-Whetham and Harding, was the impressario, the lynch-pin of the project, coordinating the various acts which created the building. Achieving zero defects was the aim pursued through a face to face approach that seems to have worked well. The management contract system has not always been well received by architects, whose traditional dominance is threatened, but it reflects the ever-growing complexity of the construction process. Teamwork is at the core of this approach. The team was something more than a well-intentioned fiction at Vauxhall Cross. The schedule was tight and there was a lot to build, but it was done, to cost and on time. Having good listeners in Regalian was essential, say Boddam-Whetham and Harding. There was a confidence throughout that the client understood the problems and would respond.

It will be a year or two before the users of the building will be able to judge its success in meeting their needs. But it is obvious that Vauxhall Cross is one of a new generation of government buildings, reflecting a recognition that staff in private and public sectors now expect good working conditions.

It is not too early, however, to make some assessment of the scheme's impact on the surrounding area. The view across the river from the Tate Gallery is famously depressing. If the Millbank Tower on the north bank is one of the better London buildings of the 1960s, the Albert Embankment provides clear corroboration of the disastrous effects of the last but one property boom on the capital. None of the buildings here is better than mediocre. None attempts even a gesture to the street or to the passer-by. Around the foot of Vauxhall Bridge, the confusion is abject as huge areas of road twist around and under the solid barrier of the railway tracks. Noise and air pollution are disturbingly high. Preliminary research revealed that a prime source of streaking on the new building would be the black deposits given off by trains braking to stop at Vauxhall Station. It was not within the power of Regalian to change any of this. There is a certain defensive quality about Farrell's building that seems appropriate to the location; witness his criticisms of the unthinking (as he sees it) modernist concern for light and air. It is the solidity of Vauxhall Cross that gives the building the authority it needs, in view of its difficult location. The first (residential) scheme had something of this authority, albeit expressed in a more openly post modernist way. Nobody will now live in Vauxhall Cross, but it has retained just a hint of the "village" that might have been built on the site.

Superficially, however, the image of the building is one of strength: a portal guarding the way across the bridge. It provides an anchor, a point of identity in the midst of visual anarchy. Whether its architectural themes will be taken up when the drab office slabs of the 1960s that are its neighbours are finally replaced, is impossible to predict. Two features of the building should, however, be regarded as a benchmark for further developments in the area. First, its scale is right for the riverside. The Thames is a big river and small buildings (like some of the housing in Docklands) look lost alongside it. Stepping the building back from the river in stages is a mark of respect for the views along and across the bends in the Thames. The south elevation is entirely different: its strong verticality responds to the bleak roadscape it faces. Secondly, the provision of a public

walkway along the river is, though something of a token gesture, a blow for public accessibility. The Victoria Embankment had little impact on the South Bank, but the future is certain to see a new walkway along much of the Thames from Docklands to Battersea. The Royal Fine Art Commission, charged by its Royal Charter to represent the interests of the public in development schemes, played a significant role in seeing the scheme to fruition.

Vauxhall Cross has been completed at a critical time for the construction industry in Britain. The London building boom of the 1980s is over and its consequences are already being critically assessed. The key issues for the 1990s are, first, the balance between the private and the public domain and, second, the relationship between the building and the urban fabric that surrounds it. Neither of these matters has anything to do with the stylistic concerns that obsessed so many critics of architecture during the 1980s. The development industry is being asked to come up with a better product at a time of falling returns. Vauxhall Cross is a striking new public building, skilfully tailored for the needs of its users, which has already given identity to one of London's most anonymous fringes. It would never have been built but for the negotiating skills, determination and commitment to quality of David Goldstone and his colleagues at Regalian. They have succeeded in completing a building of distinction in difficult times, and making it pay. After all the delays, the discussions and the controversies, Vauxhall Cross is a building of which London can be proud.

Drawings

The realisation of Vauxhall Cross involved the
preparation of thousands of sketches, presentation,
working and detail drawings. The following selection of
presentation and scope drawings prepared by Terry
Farrell & Company illustrate the main design features
of the project.

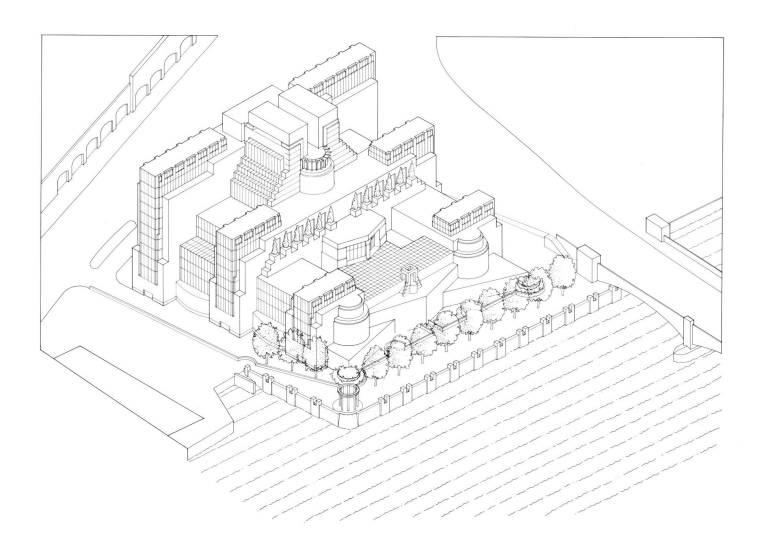

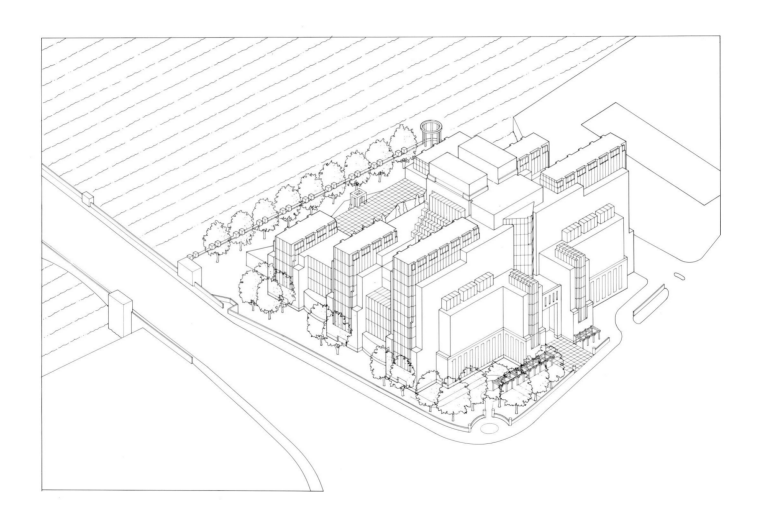

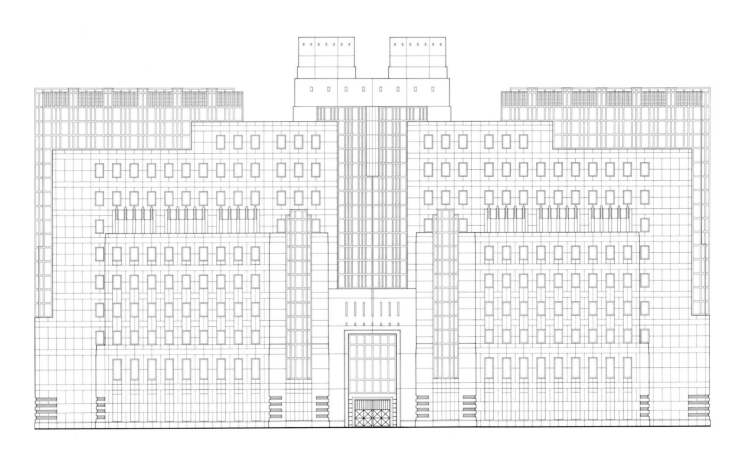

**River elevation
(North)**

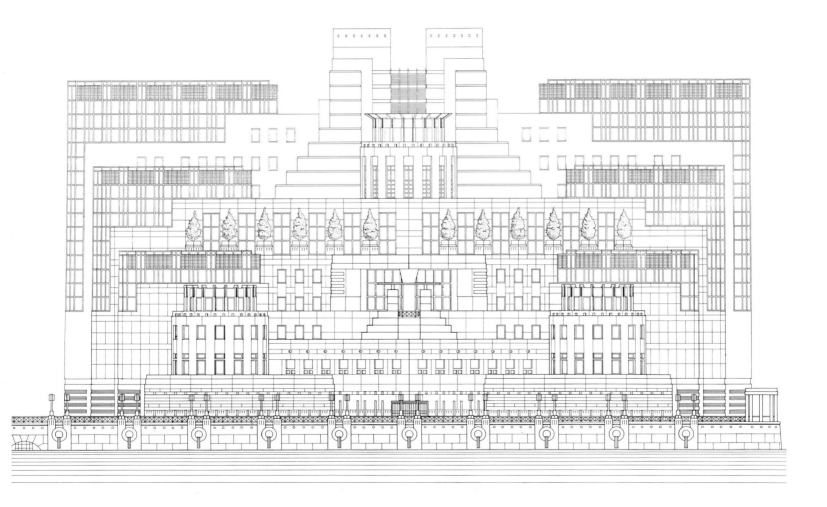

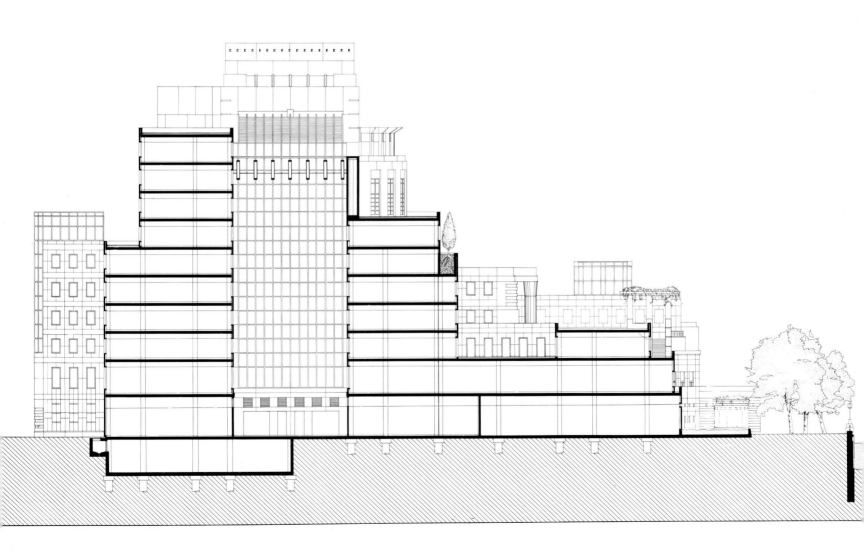

Below:
Detail of the Albert
Embankment
entrance
Far right:
Detail of the River
elevation

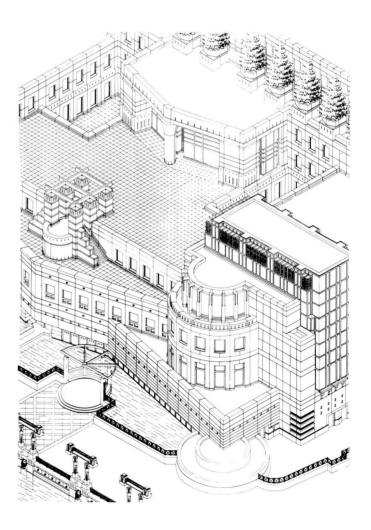

Project team

Dick Woods
Regalian Properties PLC

Regalian Properties plc

Mike Baxter
Ed Badke
David Goldstone
Lee Goldstone
Simon Hill
Lewis Jones
Roland King
Stephen Marshall
Alan Morgan
David Owen
Alison Paterson
Bob Perdeaux
Dick Woods

Toby Bridge
Terry Farrell & Co.

Terry Farrell & Co

Teresa Ashton
Christian Bechtle
Paul Bell
Marc Berg
Andy Bow
Toby Bridge
Steve Brown
John Campbell
John Chatwin
Philip Chester
Arturo Cogollo
Andrew Culpeck
Andrew Culham
Llana Durovic
Helen Espey
Terry Farrell
Tye Farrow
D'Arcy Fenton
Grace Ford
Lionel Friedland
Sharon Galvin
Ivan Green
Josephine Guckian
Trevor Hall
Kai Hansen
Peter Hulbert
Maria Iwanicki
Tom Kimbell
Sebastian Klatt

Elke Knoesz
Stefan Krummeck
Marcus Kuhn
Colin Laine
Simon Loring
Barry Macken
Justin Mueller
Tom Mulligan
Dominic Papa
Christos Papaloizou
Sharon Phillips
Elizabeth Pienaar
Thomas Ringhof
Walter Seward
Doug Streeter
Greg Talmont
Ashok Tendle
Tim Thompson
Ivan Turcinov
Jon Wallsgrove
Vincent Westbrook
Duncan Whatmore
Clive Wilkinson
Gary Young
Nigel Young
Stefan Zalewski

Ove Arup & Partners

Gert Andresen
Anita Batterham
Ray Bennett
Parminder Bhogal
Gary Bird
John Blanchard
Fred Brenchley
Rod Bryenton
Lee Carter
Guy Channer
Georgina Cockroft
Judy Coleman
John Coppin
Don Davidson
Phil Dilley
Brian Egan
Martin Fenn
Giovanni Festa
Terry Fitzgerald
Alan Foster
Rick Garrett
Mike Glover
Alistair Guthrie
Patrick Hayes
Robert Hide
Doug Hobbs
Nick Howard
Nick Koor
William Lai

Brian Lieberman
Peter O'Riordan
Julian Olley
Richard Purdy
Alan Reading
Stephen Rooney
David Spencer
Mannam Shah
Peter Soar
Christine Taig
Robert Venning
Francis Walley
Jim Warne
Alex Wong

Julian Olley
Ove Arup & Partners

Cyril Sweett & Partners

Stephen Arbiter
Bob Armstrong
Jane Barclay
Michael Connolly
Barry Cotty
Maggie Crosland
Simon Darnell
Stephen Davies
John Fulton
Paul Hallam
Martin Hawkins
John Higginson
David Hossack
Peter Hudson
Reza Kahn
Ian Keogh
Nick Kilsby
Ian Kingdon
Michael Lyons
Christopher Meara
Michael Moorhead
Alan Morris
Sheila Peacock
David Pool
Stephen Roberts
Allison Raby
Jeremy Roden
Tom Shaw

Peter Shrubb
Roy Tolen
Roberta Warwick
Malcolm Walker
Purdie Woochit

Stephen Arbiter
Cyril Sweett & Partners

Simon Harding
Laing Management Ltd

Paul Boddam-Whetham
Laing Management Ltd

Laing Management Ltd

Colin Acus
Tom Adams
Anita Atkinson
Andy Bacon
Paul Banyard
Russell Bates
Gary Bibby
Paul Boddam-Whetham
Sharon Brewster
Ian Budd
Frank Carroll
Raj Chaman
Dennis Clarke
John Connolly
Kevin Cowley
Barry Day
Jean-Michel Dumolard
Alistair Duthart
Ken Essien
Graham Glassey
Ron Gorrod
Kevin Grogan
Simon Harding
John Hay
John Hodson
John Holt
Mark Hunter

Graham Inkersole
Nicola Jenn
Lesley Joiner
Paul Judd
Keith Kearley
Dave Leigh
Yannick L'Loch
Sue Lovell
Roy Mellor
Ian Nicholls
Les Noakes
Ian Norbury
Alan Ormston
Steve Pakes
Charles Richmond
Mark Rowe
Ashan Sattar
Mike Schonut
Dave Stevens
John Trounce
Ray Ubaniak
John Walsh
Kim Whitehead
Amanda Williams
Maxine Wyer

Works Contracters

Paul Banyard &
Associates
M.J. Clancy Ltd.
A.Davies & Co
(Shopfitters) Ltd.
Empire Stone Ltd.
EPL
Fairclough Civil
Engineering Ltd.
Haden Young Ltd
How Lindner plc
Kobi Cradles Ltd.
Linvar Ltd.
Phoenix Electrical Co. Ltd.
Prater Roofing Ltd.
Hans Schmidlin (UK) Ltd.
Siddeley Landscapes Ltd.
Singer & James Ltd.
Stent Foundations Ltd.
System Floors Ltd.
Swift Structures Ltd.
Thermofelt (Contracts) Ltd
Thyssen Lifts &
Escalators Ltd.
Vogue Development Co.
Ltd.
Wimpey Plant & Transport
Ltd.